MATHEMATICS COUNTS 4A

A Topical Approach

Gopi Krishnan

SNP
Panpac

An imprint of SNP Panpac Pte Ltd

SNP Panpac Pte Ltd
97 Ubi Avenue 4
Singapore 408754

© SNP Panpac Pte Ltd

Website: http://www.snpcorp.com
Email: panpmktg@snpcorp.com

Editor: Ang Wee Wee

First published 2004

Printed by Mainland Press Pte Ltd

ISBN 981-252-800-8

Preface

Mathematics Counts – A Topical Approach is a series of mathematics books for primary school pupils written in line with the latest syllabus set by the *Ministry of Education*.

For each topic, well-graded exercises, useful notes and worked examples, are given to help pupils understand the mathematical concepts. Examination papers and revision papers are also provided. *Mathematics Counts – A Topical Approach* aims to help pupils enhance their problem-solving skills in word problems, besides equipping them with the foundation skills in acquiring *number sense* — at home with numbers.

Problems marked with asterisk (*) are more challenging. Some *enrichment activities* are provided to cater for the more able pupils.

It is hoped that *Mathematics Counts – A Topical Approach* will help lay a good foundation for pupils to be motivated to learn mathematics, and enjoy the subject.

Contents

Chapter 1

Numbers to 100 000

Counting

A 5-digit number is made up of 5 digits. Each digit has a place value of ten thousands, thousands, hundreds, tens and ones.

Example 1

64 753 can also be written as sixty-four thousand seven hundred and fifty-three.

In 64 753, the place value of each digit is as follows:
the digit 6 is in the ten thousands place, its value is 60 000;
the digit 4 is in the thousands place, its value is 4000;
the digit 7 is in the hundreds place, its value is 700;
the digit 5 is in the tens place, its value is 50;
the digit 3 is in the ones place, its value is 3.

Exercise 1

Fill in the blanks.

1. In 89 632,

   the value of the digit 8 is _____.

   the value of the digit 9 is _____.

   the value of the digit 6 is _____.

   the value of the digit 3 is _____.

   the value of the digit 2 is _____.

2. In 20 495,

the value of the digit 2 is _____.

the value of the digit 0 is _____.

the value of the digit 4 is _____.

the value of the digit 9 is _____.

the value of the digit 5 is _____.

3. In 15 831,

the value of the digit 1 is _____.

the value of the digit 5 is _____.

the value of the digit 8 is _____.

the value of the digit 3 is _____.

the value of the digit 1 is _____.

4. In 5769,

the value of the digit 5 is _____.

the value of the digit 7 is _____.

the value of the digit 6 is _____.

the value of the digit 9 is _____.

Exercise 2

Write down the missing numbers in the following.

1. 25 761 = 20 000 + _____ + 700 + 60 + 1

2. 8934 = _____ + 900 + 30 + 4

3. 682 = 600 + _____ + 2

4. 97 = 90 + _____

Exercise 3

Fill in the blanks.

1. 30 000 + 6000 + 500 + 80 + 2 = _____

2. 70 000 + 60 = _____

3. 4000 + 500 + 90 = _____

4. 900 + 70 + 1 = _____

Exercise 4

Write the following in words.

1. 641 _____

2. 3685 _____

3. 40 999 _____

4. 62 875 _____

5. 95 892 _____

Exercise 5

Write the following in figures.

1. Three thousand two hundred _____

2. One thousand three hundred and one _____

3. Forty thousand one hundred and six _____

4. Ninety-five thousand three hundred and fifty-four _____

5. Eighty-seven thousand one hundred and sixty-two _____

Comparing and Ordering

When comparing 5-digit numbers, we look at the digits in the ten thousands place first followed by the digits in the thousands place and so on.

Exercise 6

Fill in the blanks.

1. Which number is smaller, 769 or 768? _____

2. Which number is larger, 8641 or 8651? _____

3. Which number is smaller, 89 421 or 88 301? _____

4. Which number is larger, 9036 or 9086? _____

Exercise 7

Arrange the following in ascending order.

1. 84 360, 84 361, 84 359, 84 358

_____

2. 629, 631, 630, 628

_____

3. 5219, 5220, 5222, 5218

_____

4. 98 999, 98 989, 98 979, 98 990

_____

Exercise 8

Arrange the following in descending order.

1. 69 330, 69 350, 69 320, 69 340

   _____

2. 70 985, 70 885, 70 685, 70 785

   _____

3. 990, 980, 960, 970

   _____

4. 1250, 1252, 1240, 1242

   _____

Exercise 9

Complete the number patterns below.

1. 4750, _____, 6750, 7750, _____

2. 96 950, _____, 94 950, 93 950, _____

3. 1140, _____, 1540, 1740, _____

4. 9996, 9998, _____, 10 002, _____

5. 5200, 10 200, 15 200, _____, _____

Exercise 10

Fill in the blanks.

1. _____ is 1000 more than 55 642.

2. 36 948 is 1000 more than _____.

3. _____ is 100 less than 85 400.

4. 75 430 is 100 less than _____.

5. 98 990 is _____ more than 98 980.

Exercise 11

Fill in the blanks.

1. 30 520 + 1000 = _____

2. 64 300 + 100 = _____

3. 28 450 − 1000 = _____

4. 39 475 − 100 = _____

5. 94 975 − 10 000 = _____

Rounding Off

To round off a number to the nearest ten, we look at the digit in the ones place.
(a) If it is 5 or greater than 5, we round up to the next ten.
(b) If it is smaller than 5, we round down to the same ten.

To round off a number to the nearest hundred, we look at the digit in the tens place.
(a) If it is 5 or greater than 5, we round up to the next hundred.
(b) If it is smaller than 5, we round down to the same hundred.

Example 1

(a) 6438 is 6440 when rounded off to the nearest ten.
(b) 79 564 is 79 600 when rounded off to the nearest hundred.
(c) 991 is 990 when rounded off to the nearest ten.
(d) 63 099 is 63 100 when rounded off to the nearest hundred.

Exercise 12

Round off each number to the nearest 10.

1. 68 _____ 2. 796 _____

3. 843 _____ 4. 6429 _____

5. 88 641 _____ 6. 3045 _____

7. 9685 _____ 8. 47 902 _____

9. 68 421 _____ 10. 7599 _____

Exercise 13

Round off each number to the nearest 100.

1. 159 _____ 2. 2853 _____

3. 16 492 _____ 4. 684 _____

5. 3652 _____ 6. 1028 _____

7. 17 694 _____ 8. 449 _____

9. 643 _____ 10. 8591 _____

Exercise 14

Estimate the value of each of the following, by rounding off each number, where appropriate, to the nearest 100.

1. 6932 + 7854 $\approx$ 6900 + 7900

         = _____

2. 468 + 995 $\approx$ _____ + _____

         = _____

3. 8420 – 4985 $\approx$ _____ – _____

         = _____

4. 7638 – 5980 $\approx$ _____ – _____

         = _____

5. 87 539 + 3642 $\approx$ _____ + _____

         = _____

6. 368 + 492 + 284 $\approx$ _____ + _____ + _____

         = _____

7. 6215 + 5320 – 9852 $\approx$ _____ + _____ – _____

         = _____

8. 539 – 215 + 478 $\approx$ _____ – _____ + _____

         = _____

9. 4568 – 785 + 123 $\approx$ _____ – _____ + _____

         = _____

10. 3467 – 1001 – 1257 $\approx$ _____ – _____ – _____

         = _____

Factors

Example 1

What are the factors of 20?

$$1 \times 20 = 20$$
$$2 \times 10 = 20$$
$$4 \times 5 = 20$$

So, the factors of 20 are 1, 2, 4, 5, 10 and 20.

Example 2

What are the factors of 45?

$$1 \times 45 = 45$$
$$3 \times 15 = 45$$
$$5 \times 9 = 45$$

So, the factors of 45 are 1, 3, 5, 9, 15 and 45.

Example 3

What are the common factors of 20 and 45?

The factors of 20 are 1, 2, 4, 5 and 10.
The factors of 45 are 1, 3, 5, 9, 15 and 45.

So, the common factors of 20 and 45 are 1 and 5.

Exercise 15

Fill in the missing factors.

1. $22 = $ _____ $\times 22$

   $= 2 \times$ _____

2. $30 = 1 \times$ _____

   $= 2 \times$ _____

   $=$ _____ $\times 10$

   $= 5 \times$ _____

3. $60 = 1 \times$ _____

   $= 2 \times$ _____

   $=$ _____ $\times 20$

   $=$ _____ $\times 15$

   $=$ _____ $\times 12$

   $= 6 \times$ _____

4. $50 = $ _____ $\times 50$

   $= 2 \times$ _____

   $=$ _____ $\times 10$

5. $36 = $ _____ $\times 36$

   $= 2 \times$ _____

   $=$ _____ $\times 12$

   $=$ _____ $\times 9$

   $= 6 \times$ _____

6. $48 = 1 \times$ _____

   $= 2 \times$ _____

   $=$ _____ $\times 16$

   $=$ _____ $\times 12$

   $= 6 \times$ _____

Exercise 16

List the common factors of the following.

1. 20 and 45 _____

2. 36 and 72 _____

3. 25 and 75 _____

4. 21 and 63 _____

5. 48 and 96 _____

Exercise 17

Answer 'Yes' or 'No'.

1. Is 2 a factor of 35? _____

2. Is 3 a factor of 87? _____

3. Is 7 a factor of 98? _____

4. Is 5 a factor of 65? _____

5. Is 11 a factor of 97? _____

Multiples

Example 1

What are the multiples of 2?

$2 \times 1 = 2$
$2 \times 2 = 4$
$2 \times 3 = 6$
$2 \times 4 = 8$
$2 \times 5 = 10$

The numbers 2, 4, 6, 8 and 10 are called the multiples of 2.

Example 2

What are the multiples of 5?

$$5 \times 1 = 5$$
$$5 \times 2 = 10$$
$$5 \times 3 = 15$$
$$5 \times 4 = 20$$
$$5 \times 5 = 25$$

The numbers 5, 10, 15, 20 and 25 are called the multiples of 5.

Example 3

What are the first three common multiples of 4 and 8?

The multiples of 4 are 4, ⑧, 12, ⑯, 20, ㉔, ...
The multiples of 8 are ⑧, ⑯, ㉔, 32, 40, 48, ...

The first three common multiples of 4 and 8 are 8, 16 and 24.

Exercise 18

List the first five multiples of the following numbers.

1. 3 _____

2. 4 _____

3. 6 _____

4. 8 _____

5. 9 _____

Exercise 19

Fill in the blanks.

1. Multiples of 6 : 6, _____, 18, _____, _____

    Multiples of 12: 12, 24, _____, _____, _____

    The first two common multiples of 6 and 12 are _____ and

    _____.

2. Multiples of 5 : 5, 10, _____, _____, _____, _____

    Multiples of 10: 10, _____, 30, _____, _____

    The first three common multiples of 5 and 10 are _____,

    _____ and _____.

3. Multiples of 4 : _____, _____, 12, 16, _____

    Multiples of 8 : 8, 16, _____, _____, _____

    The first two common multiples of 4 and 8 are _____ and

    _____.

4. Multiples of 7 : 7, _____, _____, _____, _____

    Multiples of 14: 14, 28, _____, _____

    The first two common multiples of 7 and 14 are _____ and

    _____.

5. Multiples of 2 : _____, _____, _____, _____

    Multiples of 4 : _____, _____, _____, _____

    The first two common multiples of 2 and 4 are _____ and

    _____.

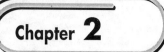

Chapter 2

Multiplication and Division I

Multiplying by a 1-digit Number

Example 1

Find the product of 4138 × 2.

$$
\begin{array}{r}
4\ 1\ {}^{1}3\ 8 \\
\times\qquad 2 \\
\hline
8\ 2\ 7\ 6 \\
\hline
\end{array}
$$

4138 × 2 = 8276

Example 2

Estimate the value of 471 × 3.

471 × 3 ≈ 500 × 3   (471 is nearer to 500 than to 400.)
        = 1500

Example 3

Estimate the value of 2161 × 3.

2161 × 3 ≈ 2000 × 3   (2161 is nearer to 2000 than to 3000.)
         = 6000

Exercise 1

Find the product of the following.

1. 2644 and 2

```
      2  6  4  4
×              2
_____

_____
```

2. 3876 and 3

```
      3  8  7  6
×              3
_____

_____
```

3. 1965 and 3

```
      1  9  6  5
×              3
_____

_____
```

4. 6423 and 4

```
      6  4  2  3
×              4
_____

_____
```

Exercise 2

Fill in the missing numbers.

1.
```
      3  5  0  2
×              5
_____
  □  □  5  □  0
_____
```

2.
```
      6  8  1  7
×              6
_____
  □  □  □  □  2
_____
```

3.
```
      4  9  3  1
×              7
_____
  □  4  □  □  □
_____
```

4.
```
      1  2  7  6
×              8
_____
  □  0  □  0  □
_____
```

Exercise 3

Estimate and then multiply.

1.   289   × 3 = _____

         ↓

   _____ × 3 ≈ _____

$$\begin{array}{r} 2\ \ 8\ \ 9 \\ \times\ \quad\quad 3 \\ \hline \end{array}$$

2.   741   × 4 = _____

         ↓

   _____ × 4 ≈ _____

$$\begin{array}{r} 7\ \ 4\ \ 1 \\ \times\ \quad\quad 4 \\ \hline \end{array}$$

3.   2893   × 4 = _____

         ↓

   _____ × 4 ≈ _____

$$\begin{array}{r} 2\ \ 8\ \ 9\ \ 3 \\ \times\ \quad\quad\quad 4 \\ \hline \end{array}$$

4.   6412   × 5 = _____

         ↓

   _____ × 5 ≈ _____

$$\begin{array}{r} 6\ \ 4\ \ 1\ \ 2 \\ \times\ \quad\quad\quad 5 \\ \hline \end{array}$$

5.   7436   × 6 = _____

         ↓

   _____ × 6 ≈ _____

$$\begin{array}{r} 7\ \ 4\ \ 3\ \ 6 \\ \times\ \quad\quad\quad 6 \\ \hline \end{array}$$

6.   8124   × 3 = _____

         ↓

   _____ × 3 ≈ _____

$$\begin{array}{r} 8\ \ 1\ \ 2\ \ 4 \\ \times\ \quad\quad\quad 3 \\ \hline \end{array}$$

7.   9896   × 7 = _____

          ↓

       _____ × 7 ≈ _____

```
          9 8 9 6
        ×       7
        ─────────
```

8.   1857   × 8 = _____

          ↓

       _____ × 8 ≈ _____

```
          1 8 5 7
        ×       8
        ─────────
```

Dividing by a 1-digit Number

Example 1

Divide 7254 by 3.

```
          2 4 1 8
      3 ) 7 2 5 4
          6
          ─────
          1 2
          1 2
          ─────
              5
              3
              ─────
                2 4
                2 4
                ─────
                  0
```

7254 ÷ 3 = 2418

Example 2

Divide the following. State the quotient and the remainder.

```
        8 5 1
  5 ) 4 2 5 8
      4 0
      ─────
        2 5
        2 5
      ─────
            8
            5
          ───
            3
          ───
```

$4258 \div 5 = 851$ R 3

When 4258 is divided by 5, the quotient is 851 and the remainder is 3.

Exercise 4

Divide the following.

1.

```
  3 ) 1  2  7  5
```

2.

```
  4 ) 6  8  3  2
```

3.

$$5 \overline{)7 \ 8 \ 1 \ 0}$$

4.

$$6 \overline{)2 \ 4 \ 2 \ 4}$$

5.

$$6 \overline{)9 \ 3 \ 4 \ 2}$$

6.

$$9 \overline{)6 \ 3 \ 2 \ 7}$$

Exercise 5

Divide the following. State the quotient and the remainder.

1. $1533 \div 5$

2. $7523 \div 4$

$$5 \overline{)1 \ 5 \ 3 \ 3}$$

3. 2472 ÷ 5

4. 9769 ÷ 6

5. 1228 ÷ 7

6. 4914 ÷ 7

Multiplying and Dividing by 10

Example 1

Multiply.

(a) $7 \times 10 = 70$
     $70 \times 10 = 700$
     $700 \times 10 = 7000$

(b) $56 \times 10 = 560$
     $560 \times 10 = 5600$

Example 2

Divide.

(a) $30 \div 10 = 3$
     $300 \div 10 = 30$
     $3000 \div 10 = 300$

(b) $690 \div 10 = 69$
     $6900 \div 10 = 690$

Example 3

Divide 5432 by 10.

(a)
```
              5 4 2
       10 ) 5 4 2 3
             5 0
            ──────
               4 2
               4 0
              ──────
                 2 3
                 2 0
                ──────
                   3
                ──────
```

$$5423 \div 10 = 542 \text{ R } 3$$

Exercise 6

Multiply the following.

1. 6×10 = _____

   60×10 = _____

   600×10 = _____

2. 9×10 = _____

   90×10 = _____

   900×10 = _____

3. 25×10 = _____

   250×10 = _____

4. 64×10 = _____

   640×10 = _____

Exercise 7

Divide the following.

1. $50 \div 10$ = _____

   $500 \div 10$ = _____

   $5000 \div 10$ = _____

2. $80 \div 10$ = _____

   $800 \div 10$ = _____

   $8000 \div 10$ = _____

3. $810 \div 10 =$ _____

$8100 \div 10 =$ _____

4. $990 \div 10 =$ _____

$9900 \div 10 =$ _____

Exercise 8

Divide the following. Then state the quotient and the remainder.

1.

$$10 \overline{)6 \ 4 \ 2 \ 7}$$

2.

$$10 \overline{)9 \ 7 \ 4 \ 6}$$

Multiplying by a 2-digit Number

Example 1

Multiply 46 by 20.

$$46 \times 20$$
$$= \underbrace{46 \times 2} \times 10$$
$$= \quad 92 \quad \times 10$$
$$= 920$$

Example 2

Multiply 365 × 60.

$$365 \times 60$$
$$= \underbrace{365 \times 6} \times 10$$
$$= 2190 \times 10$$
$$= 21\ 900$$

Example 3

Estimate and then multiply.

$$11 \times 45 \approx 10 \times 50$$
$$= 500$$

Exercise 9

Multiply the following.

1. $64 \times 20 = 64 \times 2 \times$ _____

   $= 128 \times$ _____

   $=$ _____

2. $45 \times 30 = 45 \times$ _____ $\times 10$

   $=$ _____ $\times 10$

   $=$ _____

3. $154 \times 50 = 154 \times 5 \times$ _____

   $= 770 \times$ _____

   $=$ _____

4. $460 \times 70 = 460 \times \underline{\hspace{2cm}} \times 10$

$= \underline{\hspace{2cm}} \times 10$

$= \underline{\hspace{2cm}}$

Exercise 10

Multiply the following.

1.
```
    3 5
  ×  2 4
  ─────────
```

2.
```
    6 8
  ×  3 2
  ─────────
```

3.
```
  1 2 5
  ×   4 2
  ─────────
```

4.
```
    9 9
  ×  1 6
  ─────────
```

Exercise 11

Estimate the following and then multiply.

1.   59   ×   11   = \underline{\hspace{2cm}}

    ↓   ↓

```
    5 9
  ×  1 1
  ─────────
```

\underline{\hspace{2cm}} × \underline{\hspace{2cm}} ≈ \underline{\hspace{2cm}}

2.   87   ×   31   = _____

       ↓   ↓

_____ × _____ ≈ _____

$$\begin{array}{r} 8\ 7 \\ \times\ 3\ 1 \\ \hline \end{array}$$

3.   121   ×   53   = _____

        ↓   ↓

_____ × _____ ≈ _____

$$\begin{array}{r} 1\ 2\ 1 \\ \times\ \ \ 5\ 3 \\ \hline \end{array}$$

4.   298   ×   82   = _____

        ↓   ↓

_____ × _____ ≈ _____

$$\begin{array}{r} 2\ 9\ 8 \\ \times\ \ \ 8\ 2 \\ \hline \end{array}$$

5.   311   ×   67   = _____

        ↓   ↓

_____ × _____ ≈ _____

$$\begin{array}{r} 3\ 1\ 1 \\ \times\ \ \ 6\ 7 \\ \hline \end{array}$$

6.　　793　×　89　=　_____

$$
\begin{array}{r}
7\ 9\ 3 \\
\times\ \ \ 8\ 9 \\
\hline
\end{array}
$$

_____ × _____ ≈ _____

Word Problems

Example 1

Mrs Lee bought 5 apples for $2 and 6 pears for $3. What is the difference in price between a pear and an apple?

$$200 \div 5 = 40$$
$$300 \div 6 = 50$$
$$50 - 40 = 10$$

The difference in price between a pear and an apple is 10¢.

Exercise 12

Do the following.

1.　John is twice as tall as his younger brother. If his brother is 75 cm, how tall is John?

2. A basket of fruits weighs 15 kg. If the fruits weigh 10 kg, what is the weight of 6 such empty baskets?

3. A bag contains blue marbles and black marbles. The number of blue marbles is 3 times the number of black marbles. If there are 1875 blue marbles, what is the total number of marbles in the bag?

4. A group of 9 children spaced themselves out in a row equally. If the distance between the first child and the last child was 80 m, what was the distance between the second child and the eighth child?

5. John and Henry have 1000 stamps altogether. If John has 600 stamps more than Henry, how many stamps does Henry have?

6. A fruitseller had 384 oranges. He packed some of them into 12 boxes of 24 oranges each and the remaining oranges into 6 equal bags. How many oranges were there in each bag?

Revision 1

1. Write the following in figures.

   (a) Eighty-three thousand two hundred and fifty-four _____

   (b) Six hundred forty-five thousand and twelve _____

   (c) Nine thousand seven hundred and fifteen _____

   (d) Thirty-nine thousand six hundred and twenty _____

2. Fill in the blanks.

   (a) $38\ 492 = 30\ 000 +$ _____ $+$ _____ $+$ _____ $+ 2$

   (b) $6008 =$ _____ $+ 8$

   (c) $14\ 001 = 10\ 000 +$ _____ $+$ _____

   (d) $29\ 829 =$ _____ $+$ _____ $+$ _____
       $+$ _____ $+$ _____

3. Complete the following number patterns.

   (a) 38, _____, 58, _____, _____

   (b) 10, _____, 50, 70, _____, _____

   (c) 999, _____, 799, _____, _____

   (d) _____, _____, 38, _____, 54

4. Round off the following to the nearest 10.

    (a) 88   _____

    (b) 126   _____

    (c) 3748   _____

    (d) 19 743   _____

5. Estimate the value of each of the following, by rounding off each number, where appropriate, to the nearest 100.

    (a) 2580 + 3659 $\approx$ _____ + _____

                                 $=$ _____

    (b) 1256 + 892 $\approx$ _____ + _____

                                  $=$ _____

    (c) 98 374 + 6901 $\approx$ _____ + _____

                                  $=$ _____

    (d) 9250 − 3600 $\approx$ _____ − _____

                                  $=$ _____

    (e) 6982 − 597 $\approx$ _____ − _____

                                  $=$ _____

    (f) 13 625 − 8714 $\approx$ _____ − _____

                                  $=$ _____

6. Fill in the blanks.

    (a) The factors of 12 are _____.

    (b) The factors of 15 are _____.

    (c) The common factors of 12 and 15 are _____.

    (d) Is 4 a common factor of 18 and 24? _____

7. Find the product of the following.

    (a)
$$\begin{array}{r} 2\ 6\ 8\ 9 \\ \times\qquad\ \ 6 \\ \hline \\ \hline \end{array}$$

    (b)
$$\begin{array}{r} 3\ 5\ 2\ 3 \\ \times\qquad\ \ 7 \\ \hline \\ \hline \end{array}$$

    (c)
$$\begin{array}{r} 5\ 7 \\ \times\ 2\ 0 \\ \hline \end{array}$$

    (d)
$$\begin{array}{r} 9\ 6\ 9 \\ \times\ 4\ 5 \\ \hline \end{array}$$

8. Divide the following.

(a)

$$7\overline{)2\ 1\ 2\ 8}$$

(b)

$$9\overline{)6\ 3\ 9\ 0}$$

(c)

$$8\overline{)3\ 2\ 4\ 7}$$

(d)

$$6\overline{)8\ 9\ 4\ 7}$$

9. Sandy had 345 stickers. Colin had 143 stickers. After Sandy had given Colin some stickers, they both had the same number of stickers. How many stickers did Sandy give Colin?

 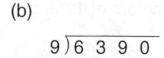

10. The total weight of Marie, Susie and Judy is 120 kg. Mary weighs thrice as much as Susie. Judy weighs 4 times as much as Susie. Find Judy's weight.

11. Ming had twice as much money as Ryan. After Ming spent $200, he had $25 less than Ryan. How much money did they have at first?

12. 2500 people took part in a cross-country race. The number of adults were 4 times the number of children. If there were 1200 men, how many women were there?

Chapter 3

Fractions

Adding and Subtracting Fractions

Fractions having the same denominator are called like fractions.
Related fractions have 1 denominator that is a factor of the other.

Example 1

Add $\frac{1}{5}$ to $\frac{2}{5}$.

$$\frac{1}{5} + \frac{2}{5}$$

$$= \frac{1 + 2}{5}$$

$$= \frac{3}{5}$$

Example 2

Subtract $\frac{2}{9}$ from $\frac{7}{9}$.

$$\frac{7}{9} - \frac{2}{9}$$

$$= \frac{7 - 2}{9}$$

$$= \frac{5}{9}$$

Example 3

Add: $1 + \frac{2}{3}$.

$$1 + \frac{2}{3}$$

$$= 1\frac{2}{3}$$

Example 4

Subtract: $1 - \dfrac{5}{7}$.

$$1 - \frac{5}{7}$$

$$= \frac{7}{7} - \frac{5}{7}$$

$$= \frac{7 - 5}{7}$$

$$= \frac{2}{7}$$

Example 5

Solve the following: $1 + \dfrac{2}{9} - \dfrac{4}{9}$.

$$1 + \frac{2}{9} - \frac{4}{9}$$

$$= 1\frac{2}{9} - \frac{4}{9}$$

$$= \frac{11}{9} - \frac{4}{9}$$

$$= \frac{5}{9}$$

Example 6

Add $\dfrac{1}{2}$ to $\dfrac{1}{6}$. Give your answer in the simplest form.

$$\frac{1}{2} + \frac{1}{6}$$

$$= \frac{3}{6} + \frac{1}{6}$$

$$= \frac{4}{6}$$

$$= \frac{2}{3}$$

Example 7

Subtract $\dfrac{2}{6}$ from $\dfrac{1}{2}$.

$$\dfrac{1}{2} - \dfrac{2}{6}$$

$$= \dfrac{3}{6} - \dfrac{2}{6}$$

$$= \dfrac{1}{6}$$

Exercise 1

Add the following fractions, giving your answers in the simplest form.

1. $\dfrac{1}{4} + \dfrac{2}{4}$

2. $\dfrac{5}{7} + \dfrac{1}{7}$

3. $\dfrac{3}{8} + \dfrac{1}{8}$

4. $\dfrac{5}{9} + \dfrac{1}{9}$

Exercise 2

Subtract the following fractions, giving your answers in the simplest form.

1. $\dfrac{5}{8} - \dfrac{2}{8}$

2. $\dfrac{4}{7} - \dfrac{2}{7}$

3. $\dfrac{9}{10} - \dfrac{5}{10}$

4. $\dfrac{11}{12} - \dfrac{5}{12}$

Exercise 3

Give your answers in the simplest form.

1. $\dfrac{1}{5} + \dfrac{2}{5} + \dfrac{1}{5}$

2. $\dfrac{2}{9} + \dfrac{3}{9} + \dfrac{1}{9}$

3. $1 - \dfrac{3}{8} - \dfrac{1}{8}$

4. $1 - \dfrac{3}{10} - \dfrac{2}{10}$

5. $1 - \dfrac{4}{6} + \dfrac{2}{6}$

6. $\dfrac{9}{12} + \dfrac{11}{12} - 1$

Exercise 4

Add or subtract the following related fractions. Give your answers in the simplest form.

1. $\dfrac{5}{8} - \dfrac{1}{2}$

   $= \dfrac{5}{8} - \dfrac{\square}{8}$

   $=$

2. $\dfrac{5}{6} - \dfrac{1}{3}$

   $= = \dfrac{5}{6} - \dfrac{\square}{6}$

   $=$

3. $\dfrac{7}{10} + \dfrac{1}{5}$

$= \dfrac{7}{10} + \dfrac{\square}{10}$

$=$

4. $\dfrac{7}{12} + \dfrac{1}{4}$

$= \dfrac{7}{12} + \dfrac{\square}{12}$

$=$

5. $\dfrac{2}{3} - \dfrac{2}{9}$

$= \dfrac{\square}{9} - \dfrac{2}{9}$

$=$

6. $\dfrac{2}{4} + \dfrac{3}{8}$

$= \dfrac{\square}{8} + \dfrac{3}{8}$

$=$

Mixed Numbers and Improper Fractions

A mixed number has a whole number part and a fractional part.

For example; $1\dfrac{3}{4}$, $2\dfrac{1}{3}$ and $5\dfrac{2}{7}$.

A fraction whose numerator is greater than or equal to the denominator is called an improper fraction.

Example 1

Write the mixed number for 3 wholes and 2 thirds.

3 wholes and 2 thirds $= 3\dfrac{2}{3}$

Example 2

Write the improper fraction for 8 quarters.

8 quarters $= \dfrac{8}{4}$

Example 3

Convert $2\frac{2}{3}$ as an improper fraction.

$$2\frac{2}{3} = 2 + \frac{2}{3}$$

$$= \frac{6}{3} + \frac{2}{3}$$

$$= \frac{8}{3}$$

Example 4

Convert $\frac{15}{6}$ as a mixed number.

$$\frac{15}{6} = \frac{12}{6} + \frac{3}{6}$$

$$= 2 + \frac{3}{6}$$

$$= 2\frac{3}{6} \text{ or } 2\frac{1}{2} \text{ (simplest form)}$$

Exercise 5

Write the mixed number for each of the following.

1. 4 wholes and 1 half = _____

2. 5 wholes and 3 fifths = _____

3. 7 wholes and 1 quarter = _____

4. 3 wholes and 5 sixths = _____

Exercise 6

Write the improper fraction for each of the following.

1. 7 thirds = _____

2. 9 quarters = _____

3. 8 fifths = _____

4. 13 sixths = _____

Exercise 7

Convert the following mixed numbers as improper fractions.

1. $2\dfrac{3}{5}$

2. $7\dfrac{2}{9}$

3. $4\dfrac{5}{6}$

4. $6\dfrac{2}{3}$

5. $8\dfrac{1}{4}$

6. $9\dfrac{1}{5}$

Exercise 8

Convert the following improper fractions as mixed numbers.

1. $\dfrac{11}{3}$

2. $\dfrac{7}{2}$

3. $\dfrac{9}{4}$

4. $\dfrac{12}{7}$

5. $\dfrac{13}{7}$

6. $\dfrac{15}{8}$

Product of a Fraction and a Whole Number

Example 1

Find the value of $\dfrac{2}{5} \times 4$.

$$\dfrac{2}{5} \times 4 = \dfrac{2 \times 4}{5 \times 1}$$

$$= \dfrac{8}{5}$$

$$= 1\dfrac{3}{5}$$

Example 2

Find the value of $6 \times \dfrac{2}{3}$.

$$6 \times \dfrac{2}{3} = \dfrac{6 \times 2}{1 \times 3}$$

$$= \dfrac{12}{3}$$

$$= 4$$

Exercise 9

Find the product of the following.

1. $\dfrac{1}{4} \times 16$

2. $\dfrac{2}{3} \times 9$

3. $\dfrac{4}{5} \times 10$

4. $\dfrac{3}{8} \times 16$

5. $\dfrac{5}{7} \times 14$

6. $\dfrac{7}{10} \times 20$

7. $8 \times \dfrac{3}{4}$

8. $12 \times \dfrac{5}{6}$

Exercise 10

Fill in the blanks.

1. There are 4 blue marbles and 12 red marbles in a bag.

   (a) Fraction of blue marbles in the bag = _____

   (b) Fraction of red marbles in the bag = _____

2. There are 6 goldfish and 9 guppies in a fish tank.

   (a) Fraction of goldfish in the tank = _____

   (b) Fraction of guppies in the tank = _____

3. In a box, there are 20 white toys, 30 red toys and the rest are green toys. There were a total of 100 toys in the box.

   (a) Number of green toys in the box = _____

   (b) Fraction of white toys in the box = _____

   (c) Fraction of red toys in the box = _____

Word Problems

Example 1

Mary had 30 toys in her cupboard. She gave away $\frac{3}{5}$ of them to her best friend.
(a) What fraction did she have left?
(b) How many toys did she give to her friend?

(a) $1 - \frac{3}{5}$

$= \frac{5}{5} - \frac{3}{5}$

$= \frac{2}{5}$

She had $\frac{2}{5}$ of her toys left.

(b) $\frac{3}{5} \times 30$

$= \frac{3 \times 30}{5 \times 1}$

$= \frac{90}{5}$

$= 18$

She gave 18 toys to her friend.

Example 2

There were a total of 120 people attending a concert and $\frac{5}{8}$ of them were adults.
(a) What fraction of children were there?
(b) How many children were attending the concert?

(a) $1 - \frac{5}{8}$

$= \frac{8}{8} - \frac{5}{8}$

$= \frac{3}{8}$

$\frac{3}{8}$ of children were there.

(b) $\frac{3}{8} \times 120$

$= \frac{3 \times 120}{8 \times 1}$

$= \frac{360}{8}$

$= 45$

45 children were attending the concert.

Exercise 11

Do the following.

1. William spent $\frac{2}{5}$ of his money on food and saved the rest. If he spent $40 on food,
   (a) how much money did he have at first?
   (b) how much money did he save?

2. A group of children went for an excursion. $\frac{1}{4}$ of them were boys. If there were a total of 50 boys at the excursion,
   (a) what fraction of the group were girls?
   (b) how many children were there altogether?

3. A housewife bought $\frac{7}{12}$ kg of meat. She also bought vegetables which were $\frac{1}{3}$ kg lighter than the meat.
   (a) What was the mass of the vegetables?
   (b) What was the total mass of the meat and vegetables?

4. Jennifer went shopping with $240. She spent $\frac{3}{8}$ of her money on a handbag and $\frac{5}{6}$ of her remaining money on a blouse. She spent the rest of her money on 2 identical hats. Find
   (a) the cost of the handbag,
   (b) the cost of the blouse,
   (c) the cost of each hat.

5. Stephanie had a box of beads. She gave $\frac{1}{6}$ of the beads to Jessie and $\frac{1}{3}$ to Amanda. She then had 27 beads left.
   (a) What fraction of the beads did she give away?
   (b) What fraction of the beads had she left?
   (c) How many beads were there in the box at first?

Chapter 4

Tables and Graphs

Tables

Data can be organised and presented for convenience by means of a table.

Exercise 1

1. A man bought 5 red marbles, 6 blue marbles, 3 yellow marbles and 4 green marbles. Using the information above, complete the table below and answer the following questions.

Colour	Red	Blue	Yellow	Green
Number of marbles				

(a) Which coloured marble did he buy the most? _____

(b) Which coloured marble did he buy the least? _____

(c) What was the total number of marbles that he bought?

_____

2. The table below shows the number of pets kept by Jack, John, Jim and Jason. By referring to the table below, answer the following questions.

Name	Jack	John	Jim	Jason
Number of pets	4	6	3	2

(a) How many pets were there altogether? _____

(b) How many children kept more than 3 pets? _____

(c) How many more pets did John have than Jason?

_____

3. The table below shows the number of cups of drinks sold in a canteen from Monday to Friday. By referring to the table below, answer the following questions.

Days	Monday	Tuesday	Wednesday	Thursday	Friday
Number of cups of drinks	20	50	60	10	30

(a) What was the total number of cups of drinks sold?

_____

(b) What was the total number of cups of drinks sold from Wednesday to Friday? _____

(c) How many more cups of drinks were sold on Tuesday than on Thursday? _____

4. The table shows the quantity of 4 kinds of fruit that were sold in a supermarket. By referring to the table below, answer the following questions.

Types of fruit	Papaya	Durian	Apple	Orange
Quantity	25	10	30	15

(a) What was the total number of fruits sold? _____

(b) Which was the most popular fruit? _____

(c) Which was the least popular fruit? _____

(d) What fraction of the total fruits sold were papayas?

_____

Bar Graphs

Data from a table can be represented as vertical bars called bar graphs or bar charts.

Exercise 2

1. Using the data in the table below, complete the bar graph.

Shirts	A	B	C	D
Number of shirts sold	4	6	7	3

(a)

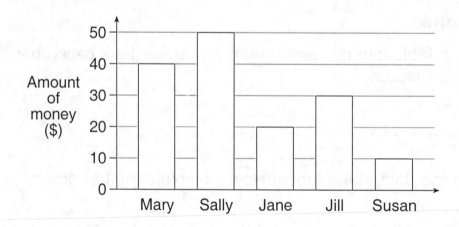

Number of shirts sold

Shirts

(b) What is the total number of shirts sold? _____

2. The bar graph shows the amount of money saved by 5 girls each month. Study it carefully and answer the questions that follow.

Amount of money ($)

Mary   Sally   Jane   Jill   Susan

(a) How much did Sally save? _____

(b) Who saved the least amount of money? _____

(c) Who saved the most amount of money? _____

(d) What is the total amount of money saved by the 5 girls?

_____

3. The bar graph shows the number of adults visiting the zoo from January to May. Complete the table below and answer the following questions.

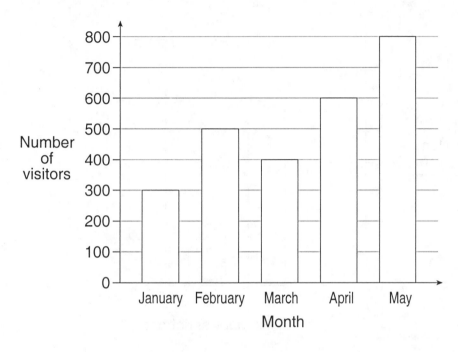

Month	January	February	March	April	May
Number of visitors					

(a) What is the total number of adult visitors from January to May?

_____

(b) In which month did the zoo have the most number of visitors?

_____

(c) In which month did the zoo have the least number of visitors?

_____

4. The girls in a class are each asked how many ribbons they own. The bar graph shows the results of this survey. Complete the table below and answer the following questions.

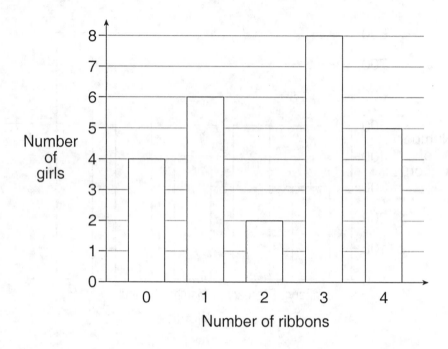

Number of ribbons

Number of ribbons	0	1	2	3	4
Number of girls					

(a) What is the total number of girls in the survey? _____

(b) How many girls have more than 2 ribbons? _____

(c) How many girls do not have any ribbons? _____

Chapter 5

Angles

Naming Angles

There are 3 ways in which an angle can be named.

Example 1

In the diagram, the angle can be named as:

(a) $\angle x$,
(b) $\angle ABC$,
(c) $\angle CBA$.

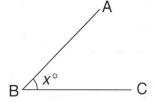

Example 2

In the diagram, the angle can be named as:

(a) $\angle y$,
(b) $\angle PQR$,
(c) $\angle RQP$.

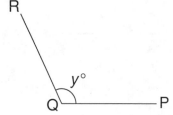

Exercise 1

By referring to the diagrams, name the angles in 3 different ways.

1. (a) _____

   (b) _____

   (c) _____

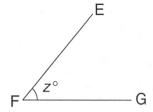

2. (a) _____

   (b) _____

   (c) _____

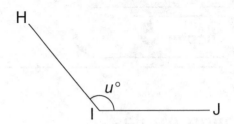

3. (a) _____

   (b) _____

   (c) _____

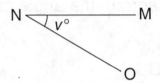

4. (a) _____

   (b) _____

   (c) _____

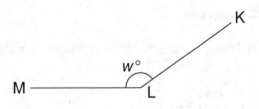

5. (a) _____

   (b) _____

   (c) _____

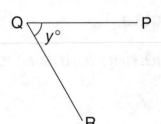

Estimating and Measuring Angles

A right angle is equal to 90°, or $\frac{1}{4}$-turn.

2 right angles are equal to 180°, or $\frac{1}{2}$-turn.

3 right angles are equal to 270°, or $\frac{3}{4}$-turn.

4 right angles are equal to 360°, or 1 whole turn.

Exercise 2

Measure the marked angles.

1. $\angle p =$ _____ °

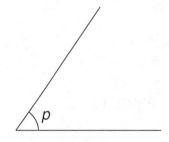

2. $\angle q =$ _____ °

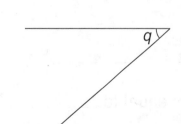

3. $\angle r =$ _____ °

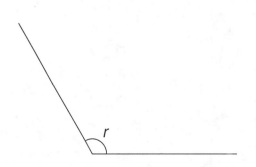

4. ∠s = _____°

![clipboard] **Exercise 3**

What is the size of each angle?

1. ∠x = _____°

   It is equal to _____ right angles.

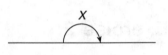

2. ∠y = _____°

   It is equal to _____ right angles.

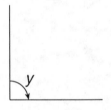

3. ∠z = _____°

   It is equal to _____ right angles.

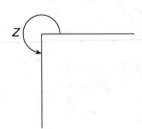

Drawing Angles

A protractor is an instrument used to measure and draw angles.

Exercise 4

1. Using a protractor, draw the following angles.

    (a) 30 °

    (b) 60 °

    (c) 135 °

    (d) 150 °

Chapter 6

Perpendicular and Parallel Lines

Perpendicular Lines

When 2 straight lines meet at a right angle, they are known as perpendicular lines.

In the diagram below, AB is perpendicular to CD.

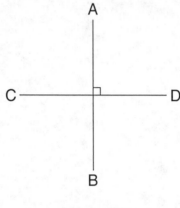

AB ⊥ CD

Exercise 1

Name each pair of perpendicular lines.

1.

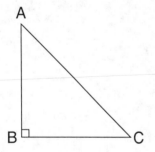

_____ ⊥ _____

2.

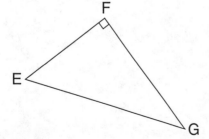

_____ ⊥ _____

3.

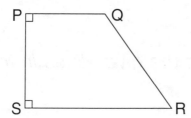

(a) _____ ⊥ _____

(b) _____ ⊥ _____

4.

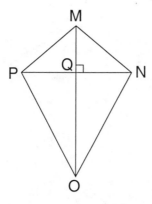

_____ ⊥ _____

Exercise 2

Using a set-square and a ruler, draw the following lines.

1. A pair of perpendicular lines.

2. A line perpendicular to the line XY passing through point A.

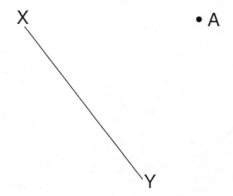

Exercise 3

Draw a perpendicular line to each of the given lines in the figures below.

1.

A————————B

2.

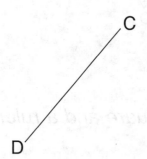

3.

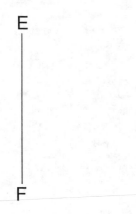

4.

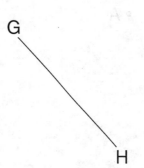

Parallel Lines

Parallel lines are lines that remain at the same distance apart and never meet.

Exercise 4

Name each pair of parallel lines in the diagrams below.

1.

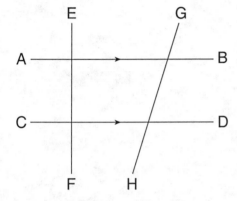

_____ // _____

2.

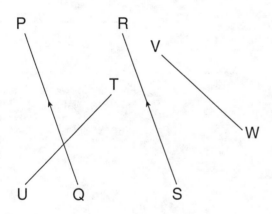

_____ // _____

3.

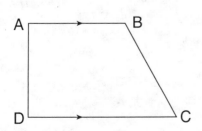

_____ // _____

4.

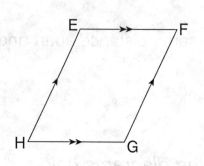

(a) _____ // _____

(b) _____ // _____

5.

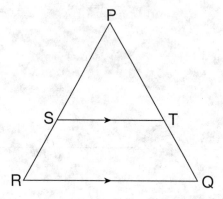

_____ // _____

6.

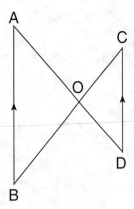

_____ // _____

Exercise 5

Using a set-square and a ruler, draw the following lines.

1. A pair of parallel lines.

2. A line parallel to the given line XY and passing through point P.

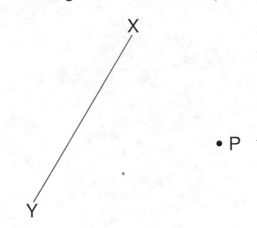

Exercise 6

Draw a line parallel to each of the given lines.

1.

2.

C————————————D

3.

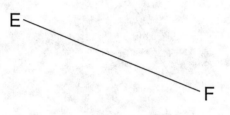

E

F

4.

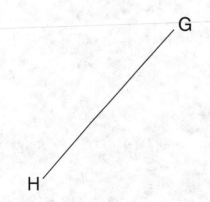

G

H

Rectangles

Perimeter of a rectangle = 2 × Sum of length and breadth

Area of a rectangle = Length × Breadth

Example 1

The length of a rectangle is 8 cm and its breadth is 3 cm. Find
(a) its perimeter,
(b) its area.

(a) Perimeter of the rectangle = 2 × (8 + 3)
$$= 2 \times 11$$
$$= 22 \text{ cm}$$

(b) Area of the rectangle = 8 × 3
$$= 24 \text{ cm}^2$$

Example 2

The area of a rectangle is 40 cm². If its breadth is 5 cm, find
(a) its length,
(b) its perimeter.

(a) Length $= \dfrac{\text{Area}}{\text{Breadth}}$

$$= \dfrac{40}{5}$$
$$= 8 \text{ cm}$$

(b) Perimeter = 2 × (8 + 5)
$$= 2 \times 13$$
$$= 26 \text{ cm}$$

Example 3

The perimeter of a rectangle is 60 cm. If its length is 20 cm, find
(a) its breadth,
(b) its area.

(a) Length + Breadth = 60 ÷ 2
$$= 30 \text{ cm}$$

Breadth = 30 − 20
$$= 10 \text{ cm}$$

(b) Area of the rectangle = 20 × 10
$$= 200 \text{ cm}^2$$

Exercise 1

1. The area of a rectangular piece of paper is 80 cm². If its length is 16 cm, find (a) its breadth,
(b) its perimeter.

2. The perimeter of a rectangle is 96 cm. If its breadth is 18 cm, find (a) its length,
(b) its area.

3. In the diagram below, the breadth of a rectangle is 6 cm. If its length is twice its breadth, find
   (a) its length,
   (b) its perimeter,
   (c) its area.

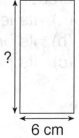

6 cm

Rectangle

4. The perimeter of a rectangle is 42 cm. If its length is twice its breadth, find
   (a) its length,
   (b) its breadth,
   (c) its area.

*5. The area of a rectangle is 75 cm^2. If its length is thrice its breadth, find
  (a) its length,
  (b) its breadth,
  (c) its perimeter.

*6. A rectangular floor measures 12 m by 10 m. A rectangular carpet measuring 8 m by 5 m is placed in the middle of the room, as shown in the diagram. Find the area of the room not covered by the carpet.

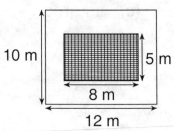

EPB

*7. The floor of a rectangular room measures 12 m by 8 m. If it costs $10 to tile 1 m^2 of the floor, find
   (a) the area of the floor,
   (b) the cost of tiling the floor.

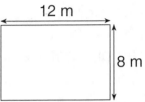

*8. The figure shows a rectangular field with a path around it. The path is 2 m wide and covered with tiles at $20 per m^2. Find
   (a) the area of the field (excluding the path),
   (b) the cost of tiling the path.

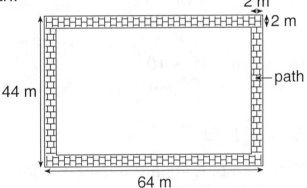

Squares

Perimeter of a square = 4 × Length

Area of a square = Length × Breadth

Example 1

The length of a square is 6 cm. Find
(a) its area,
(b) its perimeter.

(a) Area = 6 × 6
             = 36 cm^2

(b) Perimeter = 4 × 6
                      = 24 cm

Example 2

A piece of wire 40 cm long is bent to form a square. Find
(a) its length,
(b) its area.

(a) Length = 40 ÷ 4
                 = 10 cm

(b) Area = 10 × 10
             = 100 cm^2

Example 3

The area of a square is 64 cm. Find
(a) its length,
(b) its perimeter.

(a)   64 = 8 × 8
         Length = 8 cm

(b) Perimeter = 4 × 8
                      = 32 cm

Exercise 2

1. The length of a square is 6 cm. Find
   (a) its perimeter,
   (b) its area.

2. The perimeter of a square is 40 cm. Find
   (a) its length,
   (b) its area.

3. The area of a square is 64 cm^2. Find
   (a) its length,
   (b) its perimeter.

4. A piece of wire 60 cm long is bent to form a square. Find
   (a) its length,
   (b) its area.

5. A man ran around a square field 4 times and covered a distance of 320 m. Find
   (a) the length of the field,
   (b) the area of the field.

6. A rectangle and a square have the same area. If the rectangle measures 20 cm by 5 cm, find
   (a) the area of the square,
   (b) the length of the square,
   (c) the perimeter of the square.

Composite figures

Example 1

In the diagram shown, find (a) its perimeter,
(b) its area.

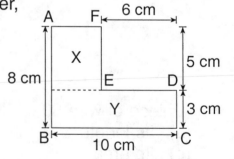

(a) Perimeter of the figure
    = 8 + 10 + 3 + 6 + 5 + 4
    = 36 cm

(b) Area of the figure
    = Area of rectangle X + Area of rectangle Y
    = (5 × 4) + (10 × 3)
    = 20 + 30
    = 50 cm^2

EPB

Exercise 3

Find the perimeter of the following figures.

1.

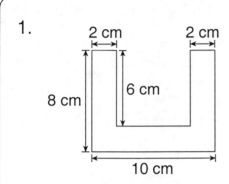

Perimeter =

2.

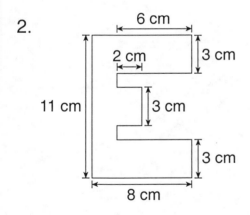

Perimeter =

Exercise 4

Find the area of the following figures.

1.

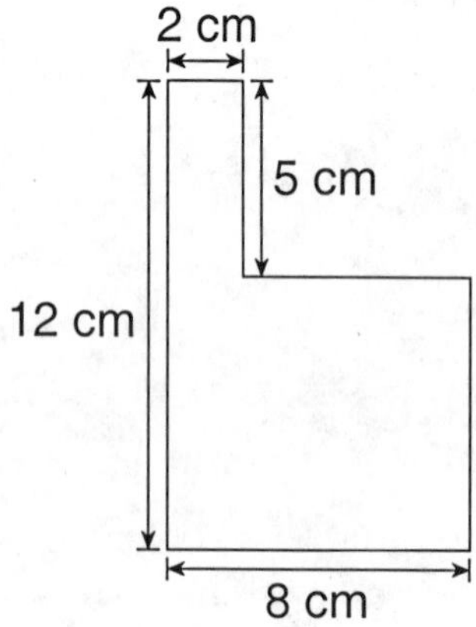

2 cm

5 cm

12 cm

8 cm

Area =

2.

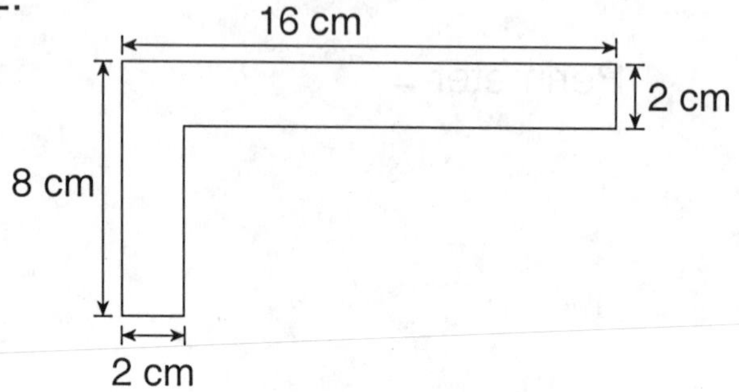

16 cm

2 cm

8 cm

2 cm

Area =

Exercise 5

Find (a) the area,
        (b) the perimeter of the figure below.

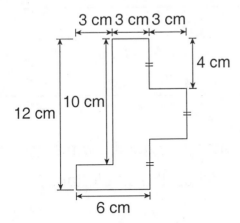

Exercise 6

Find (a) the area,
        (b) the perimeter of the unshaded region in the figure below.

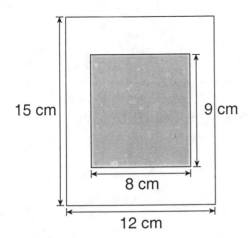

Revision 2

1. (a) List all the factors of 32.

   _____

   (b) List the first 5 multiples of 15.

   _____

2. A tank which contains 350 litres of water is $\frac{5}{7}$ full. How many more litres of water must be added to fill up the whole tank?

3. Tick the angles which are bigger than a $\frac{1}{4}$-turn.

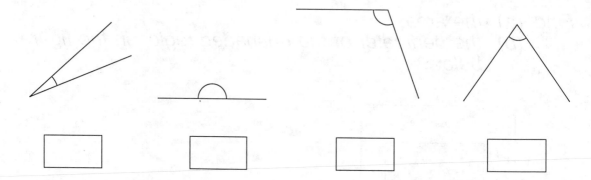

4. Name the pair of perpendicular lines in the figure below.

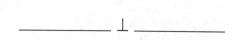

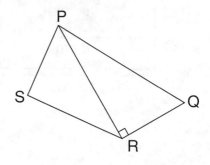

5. Gina earned $800 per month. She spent $\frac{1}{2}$ of it on food and $\frac{3}{8}$ of the remaining money on transport. How much money had she left?

6. The bar graph below shows the popularity of certain sports in a school. Study the graph carefully and answer the following questions.

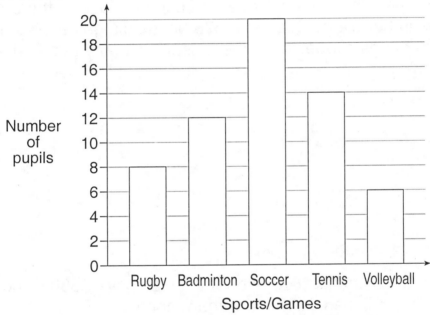

(a) Find the total number of pupils in the survey.   _____

(b) Which is the most popular sport in the school?   _____

(c) How many pupils participated in Volleyball?

    _____

(d) Which game is more popular, Badminton or Tennis?

    _____

7. $\frac{3}{5}$ of the people at a dinner party are women, and the rest are men. If there are 150 women, how many men are there?

8. Mrs Tan gave the same number of beads to each of the 8 children in her class. She gave 375 beads altogether to the boys and 225 beads altogether to the girls. How many beads did each child get?

9. Fiona and Gail had $3860 altogether. Gail gave $360 to her mother and still had $200 more than Fiona.
   (a) How much money did Fiona have?
   (b) How much money did Gail have at first?

10. Mary baked 260 biscuits. After giving a certain number of biscuits to 5 of her friends equally, she had 45 biscuits left. How many cookies did each of her friends get?

11. A rectangular poster has a length of 8 cm and an area of 128 cm². Find its perimeter.

12. A rectangular floor is 8 m long and 7 m wide. A square rug of length 4 m is laid on the floor. What is the area of the floor not covered by the rug?

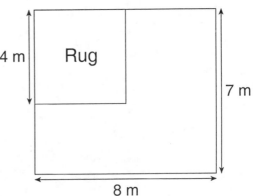

4 m | Rug

7 m

8 m

13. Find the perimeter of the figure below.

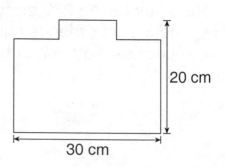

14. Find the perimeter of the figure below.

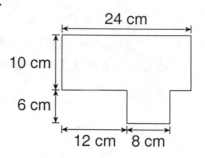

15. The figure below shows the dimension of a garden. Find the total cost of covering the garden with carpet grass if it costs $12 per m².

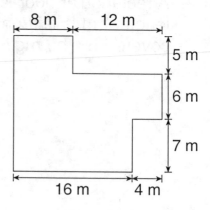

16. The areas of square BCDE and rectangle ABEF are 64 cm² and 144 cm² respectively. What is the length of AB?

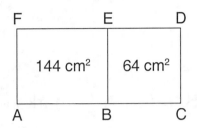

17. Alex has 5 times as many stamps as Andrew. Andrew has half as many stamps as Harry. If Alex has 432 stamps more than Andrew, how many stamps does Harry have?

18. Michelle, Ben and Steven won a total of 579 stickers at a funfair. If Michelle won 124 stickers more than Ben and Steven won 118 stickers fewer than Ben, how many stickers did Ben and Steven win altogether?

Mid-Year Examination

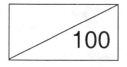

Section A (2 marks each)

Choose the correct answers, and write its number in the brackets provided.

1. 40 819 written in words is _____.
   (1) four thousand eight hundred and nineteen
   (2) fourteen thousand eight hundred and ninety
   (3) forty thousand eight hundred and nineteen
   (4) forty-eight thousand and nineteen ( )

2. 40 000 + 8000 + 9 = _____
   (1) 40 809   (2) 48 009
   (3) 40 089   (4) 48 090 ( )

3. 20 tens + 3 ones is the same as _____.
   (1) 23   (2) 203
   (3) 2003   (4) 230 ( )

4. 6 is a common factor of _____.
   (1) 2 and 3   (2) 2, 3 and 6
   (3) 6 and 20   (4) 12, 18 and 30 ( )

5. When 12 twos are multiplied by 9, the answer is _____.
   (1) 18   (2) 24
   (3) 108   (4) 216 ( )

6. Amy earns $4500 a month. Every month she spends half of it, pays $600 for rent and saves the rest. How much will she save in a year?
   (1) $21 809   (2) $20 900
   (3) $19 808   (4) $19 800 ( )

7. Round off the difference between 7489 and 20 000 to the nearest 100.
   (1) 13 000
   (2) 12 600
   (3) 12 510
   (4) 12 500
   (   )

8. The product of 12 and 19 is _____.
   (1) 208
   (2) 400
   (3) 228
   (4) 330
   (   )

9. Express $7\frac{2}{9}$ as an improper fraction.
   (1) $\frac{14}{9}$
   (2) $\frac{65}{9}$
   (3) $\frac{60}{7}$
   (4) $\frac{55}{6}$
   (   )

10. In $\frac{27}{9} = \frac{\square}{3}$, what is the missing number?
    (1) 5
    (2) 11
    (3) 7
    (4) 9
    (   )

11. Which one of the following is the best estimation for 596×12?
    (1) 600×10
    (2) 600×20
    (3) 500×20
    (4) 500×10
    (   )

12. The first common multiple of 8 and 12 is _____.
    (1) 2
    (2) 4
    (3) 16
    (4) 24
    (   )

13. How many hundreds are there in the product of 3625 and 4?
    (1) 300
    (2) 100
    (3) 145
    (4) 240
    (   )

14. I am standing facing East. Which direction will I face, if I make $\frac{3}{4}$ complete turn to my left?
    (1) East
    (2) West
    (3) North
    (4) South
    (   )

15. A number is between 24 and 34. It is also a multiple of 7. What is the number?
    (1) 26   (2) 28
    (3) 30   (4) 35   ( )

16. A piece of rope 36 cm long was cut into 12 equal portions. What is the total length of 2 such pieces?
    (1) 3 cm   (2) 6 cm
    (3) 12 cm   (4) 24 cm   ( )

17. The perimeter of a rectangle is 42 cm. If its length is twice its breadth, find its length.
    (1) 7 cm   (2) 10 cm
    (3) 14 cm   (4) 21 cm   ( )

18. Minghua had \$20. He used $\frac{1}{4}$ of it to buy pencils at 20¢ each. How many pencils did he buy?
    (1) 20   (2) 25
    (3) 50   (4) 60   ( )

19. Michael has 8 hours of free time every day. He spends $\frac{1}{4}$ of his free time doing his homework and 1 hour revising his work. How much free time has Michael left for other activities every day?
    (1) 3 hours   (2) 4 hours
    (3) 5 hours   (4) 6 hours   ( )

20. Linda spent $\frac{2}{9}$ of her money on a dress and $\frac{1}{3}$ of her money on a pair of shoes. What fraction of her money had she left?
    (1) $\frac{3}{9}$ (2) $\frac{4}{9}$

    (3) $\frac{5}{9}$ (4) $\frac{7}{27}$ ( )

Section B (2 marks each)

Write the correct answers in the blanks provided.

21. A piece of wire 56 cm long is bent to form a square. What is the length of one side of the square?

   _____

22. How many more $\frac{1}{2}$ litres of water must be added to an empty container to make 6 litres?

   _____

23. 45 is the fifth multiple of a certain number. What is the number?

   _____

24. What is the greatest whole number that can be placed in the box to make the number sentence below true?

   $\frac{11}{4}$ + ☐ is smaller than 6.

   _____

25. The table below shows the number of apples Tom sold from Monday to Wednesday.

Day	Number of apples
Monday	100
Tuesday	145
Wednesday	219

If he sold the apples at 50¢ each, how much money did he collect on the third day in all?

$_____

26. Draw angle XAB so that it is smaller than a right angle.

A •——————————— B

27. Express in simplest form, 20¢ as a fraction of $1.20.

_____

28. The following figure has a perimeter of 64 cm. Find the length of AB.

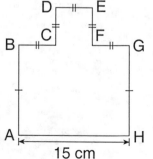

AB = _____ cm

29. Arrange the values $\frac{1}{3}$, $\frac{1}{2}$, $\frac{9}{10}$ and $\frac{3}{5}$ in ascending order.

_____

30. Every bottle of soft drink contains 285 ml of liquid. What is the total amount of drink you can get from 9 such bottles?

_____

31. The total mass of Amy and her father is 93 kg. Amy's father has a mass of 37 kg more than Amy. Find Amy's mass.

_____

32. 6 ten thousands, 2 thousands, 5 hundreds and 9 ones is equal to _____.

33. Sally bought $4\frac{1}{2}$ m of plastic to wrap her books and found that she had $1\frac{3}{5}$ m of plastic left. What is the length of plastic she used?

_____

34. Find the unshaded area of the figure below.

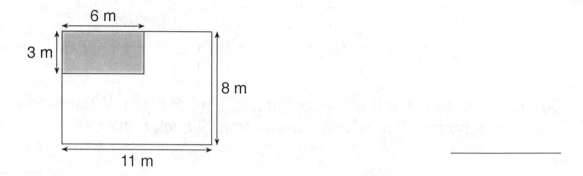

35. The bar graph below shows the number of books sold by Ibrahim in a week.

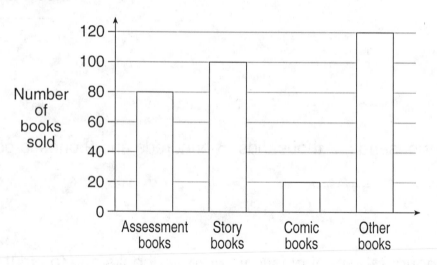

Complete the following table to show the data given in the bar graph.

Type of book	Assessment books	Story books	Comic books	Other books
Number of books sold				

Section C (5 marks each)

Do these problems.

36. A fruit seller has an equal number of apples and oranges. He
    sold 109 oranges and 45 apples. The number of apples left is
    5 times the number of oranges left. What is the total number of
    fruits he had at first?

37. A businessman saved $8400 in one year. He saved $800 a
    month for the first 9 months and an equal amount of money for
    the remaining 3 months.
    (a) How much did he save for the first 9 months?
    (b) How much did he save per month for the remaining 3
         months?

38. The length of a rectangular plot of land is 90 m long. If the breadth of the plot of land is $\frac{1}{3}$ of its length, find

(a) the breadth of the rectangular plot of land,
(b) its perimeter.

39. Name 2 pairs of perpendicular lines and 2 pairs of parallel lines found in the figure below.

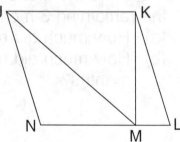

40. Using your protractor, draw and label ∠XYZ = 145° in the space below.

41. $\frac{2}{5}$ of the people present at a party are adults. The rest are children. If there are 90 children, how many more children than adults are there?

Enrichment Activities

Finding Unknown Angles

Vertically opposite angles are equal.

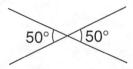

The sum of angles on a straight line is 180°.

135°   45°

$$135° + 45° = 180°$$

The sum of angles at a point is 360°.

30°

150°   180°

$$150° + 30° + 180° = 360°$$

Exercise

1. Find ∠*j* in the figure below.

    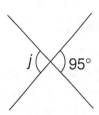

2. In the figure, ABC is a straight line and ∠DBC = 70°. Find ∠ABD.

    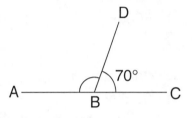

3. In the figure, ∠EFG = 90° and ∠HFG = 35°. Find ∠EFH.

    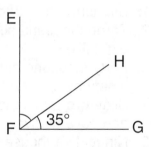

4. Find ∠*x* in the figure below.

    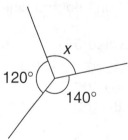

5. Find ∠*y* in the figure below.

    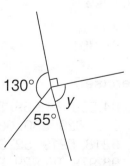

Answers

Chapter 1

Exercise 1

1. 80 000, 9000, 600, 30, 2
2. 20 000, 0, 400, 90, 5
3. 10 000, 5000, 800, 30, 1
4. 5000, 700, 60, 9

Exercise 2

1. 5000
2. 8000
3. 80
4. 7

Exercise 3

1. 36 582
2. 70 060
3. 4590
4. 971

Exercise 4

1. Six hundred and forty-one
2. Three thousand six hundred and eight-five
3. Forty thousand nine hundred and ninety-nine
4. Sixty-two thousand eight hundred and seventy-five
5. Ninety-five thousand eight hundred and ninety-two

Exercise 5

1. 3200
2. 1301
3. 40 106
4. 95 354
5. 87 162

Exercise 6

1. 768
2. 8651
3. 88 301
4. 9086

Exercise 7

1. 84 358, 84 359, 84 360, 84 361
2. 628, 629, 630, 631
3. 5218, 5219, 5220, 5222
4. 98 979, 98 989, 98 990, 98 999

Exercise 8

1. 69 350, 69 340, 69 330, 69 320
2. 70 985, 70 885, 70 785, 70 685
3. 990, 980, 970, 960
4. 1252, 1250, 1242, 1240

Exercise 9

1. 5750, 8750
2. 95 950, 92 950
3. 1340, 1940
4. 10 002, 10 004
5. 20 200, 25 200

Exercise 10

1. 56 642
2. 35 948
3. 85 300
4. 75 530
5. 10

Exercise 11

1. 31 520
2. 64 400
3. 27 450
4. 39 375
5. 84 975

Exercise 12

1. 70
2. 800
3. 840
4. 6430
5. 88 640
6. 3050
7. 9690
8. 47 900
9. 68 420
10. 7600

Exercise 13

1. 200
2. 2900
3. 16 500
4. 700
5. 3700
6. 1000
7. 17 700
8. 400
9. 600
10. 8600

Exercise 14

1. 14 800
2. 1500
3. 3400
4. 1600

5. 91 100
6. 1200
7. 1600
8. 800
9. 3900
10. 1200

Exercise 15

1. 1, 11
2. 30, 15, 3, 6
3. 60, 30, 3, 4, 5, 10
4. 1, 25, 5
5. 1, 18, 3, 4, 6
6. 48, 24, 3, 4 ,8

Exercise 16

1. 1 and 5
2. 1, 2, 3, 4, 5, 6, 9, 12, 18 and 36
3. 1, 5 and 25
4. 1, 3, 7 and 21
5. 1, 2, 3, 4, 6, 8, 12, 16, 24 and 48

Exercise 17

1. No
2. Yes
3. Yes
4. Yes
5. No

Exercise 18

1. 3, 6, 9, 12, 15
2. 4, 8, 12, 16, 20
3. 6, 12, 18, 24, 30
4. 8, 16, 24, 32, 40
5. 9, 18, 27, 36, 45

Exercise 19

1. 12, 24, 30;
   36, 48, 60;
   12 and 24
2. 15, 20, 25, 30;
   20, 40, 50;
   10, 20 and 30
3. 4, 8, 20;
   24, 32, 40;
   8 and 16
4. 14, 21, 28, 35;
   42, 56;
   14 and 28

5. 2, 4, 6, 8;
   4, 8, 12, 16;
   4 and 8

Chapter 2

Exercise 1

1. 5288
2. 11 628
3. 5895
4. 25 692

Exercise 2

1. 17 510
2. 40 902
3. 34 517
4. 10 208

Exercise 3

1. 300; 900
2. 700; 2800
3. 11 572; 3000; 12 000
4. 32 060; 6000; 30 000
5. 44 616; 7000; 42 000
6. 24 372; 8000; 24 000
7. 69 272; 10 000; 70 000
8. 14 856; 2000; 16 000

Exercise 4

1. 425
2. 1708
3. 1562
4. 404
5. 1557
6. 703

Exercise 5

1. 306 R 3
2. 1880 R 3
3. 494 R 2
4. 1628 R 1
5. 175 R 3
6. 702 R 3

Exercise 6

1. 60; 600; 6000
2. 90; 900; 9000
3. 250; 2500
4. 640; 6400

Exercise 7

1. 5; 50; 500
2. 8; 80; 800
3. 81; 810
4. 99; 990

Exercise 8

1. 642 R 7
2. 974 R 6

Exercise 9

1. 10; 10; 1280
2. 3; 135; 1350
3. 10; 10; 7700
4. 7; 3220; 32 200

Exercise 10

1. 840
2. 2176
3. 5250
4. 1584

Exercise 11

1. 649; 60, 10, 600
2. 2697; 90, 30, 2700
3. 6413; 100, 50, 5000
4. 24 436; 300, 80, 24 000
5. 20 837; 300, 70, 21 000
6. 70 577; 800, 90, 72 000

Exercise 12

1. 150 cm
2. 30 kg
3. 2500
4. 60 m
5. 200
6. 16

Revision 1

1. (a) 83 254
   (b) 645 012
   (c) 9715
   (d) 39 620

2. (a) 8000, 400, 90
   (b) 6000
   (c) 4000, 1
   (d) 20 000, 9000, 800, 20, 9

3. (a) 48, 68, 78
   (b) 30, 90, 110
   (c) 899, 699, 599
   (d) 22, 30, 46

4. (a) 90
   (b) 130
   (c) 3750
   (d) 19 740

5. (a) 6300
   (b) 2200
   (c) 105 300
   (d) 5700
   (e) 6400
   (f) 4900

6. (a) 1, 2, 3, 4, 6 and 12
   (b) 1, 3, 5 and 15
   (c) 1 and 3
   (d) No

7. (a) 16 134
   (b) 24 661
   (c) 1140
   (d) 43 605

8. (a) 304
   (b) 710
   (c) 405
   (d) 1491 R 1

9. 101

10. 60 kg

11. Ryan → $175, Ming → $350

12. 800

Chapter 3

Exercise 1

1. $\dfrac{3}{4}$
2. $\dfrac{6}{7}$
3. $\dfrac{4}{8}, \dfrac{1}{2}$
4. $\dfrac{6}{9}, \dfrac{2}{3}$

Exercise 2

1. $\dfrac{3}{8}$
2. $\dfrac{2}{7}$
3. $\dfrac{6}{12}; \dfrac{1}{2}$
4. $\dfrac{4}{10}; \dfrac{2}{5}$

Exercise 3

1. $\dfrac{4}{5}$
2. $\dfrac{6}{9}; \dfrac{2}{3}$

3. $\frac{4}{8}$; $\frac{1}{2}$

4. $\frac{5}{10}$; $\frac{1}{2}$

5. $\frac{4}{6}$; $\frac{2}{3}$

6. $\frac{8}{12}$; $\frac{2}{3}$

Exercise 4

1. 4; $\frac{1}{8}$

2. 2; $\frac{3}{6}$; $\frac{1}{2}$

3. 2; $\frac{9}{10}$

4. 3; $\frac{10}{12}$; $\frac{5}{6}$

5. 6; $\frac{4}{9}$

6. 4; $\frac{7}{8}$

Exercise 5

1. $4\frac{1}{2}$

2. $5\frac{3}{5}$

3. $7\frac{1}{4}$

4. $3\frac{5}{6}$

Exercise 6

1. $\frac{7}{3}$

2. $\frac{9}{4}$

3. $\frac{8}{5}$

4. $\frac{13}{6}$

Exercise 7

1. $\frac{13}{5}$

2. $\frac{65}{9}$

3. $\frac{29}{6}$

4. $\frac{20}{3}$

5. $\frac{33}{4}$

6. $\frac{46}{5}$

Exercise 8

1. $3\frac{2}{3}$

2. $3\frac{1}{2}$

3. $2\frac{1}{4}$

4. $1\frac{5}{7}$

5. $1\frac{6}{7}$

6. $1\frac{7}{8}$

Exercise 9

1. 4

2. 6

3. 8

4. 6

5. 10

6. 14

7. 6

8. 10

Exercise 10

1. (a) $\frac{1}{4}$

   (b) $\frac{3}{4}$

2. (a) $\frac{2}{5}$

   (b) $\frac{3}{5}$

3. (a) 50

   (b) $\frac{1}{5}$

   (c) $\frac{3}{10}$

Exercise 11

1. (a) $100

   (b) $60

2. (a) $\frac{3}{4}$

   (b) 200

3. (a) $\frac{1}{4}$ kg

   (b) $\frac{5}{6}$ kg

4. (a) $90

   (b) $125

   (c) $12.50

5. (a) $\frac{1}{2}$

   (b) $\frac{1}{2}$

   (c) 54

Chapter 4

Exercise 1

1.

Colour	Red	Blue	Yellow	Green
Number of marbles	5	6	3	4

   (a) Blue
   (b) Yellow
   (c) 18

2. (a) 15
   (b) 2
   (c) 4

3. (a) 170
   (b) 100
   (c) 40
4. (a) 80
   (b) Apple
   (c) Durian
   (d) $\frac{5}{16}$

Exercise 2

1. (a)

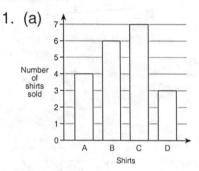

   (b) 20
2. (a) $50
   (b) Susan
   (c) Sally
   (d) $150
3. January → 300
   February → 500
   March → 400
   April → 600
   May → 800
   (a) 2600
   (b) May
   (c) January
4. 4, 6, 2, 8, 5
   (a) 25
   (b) 13
   (c) 4

Chapter 5

Exercise 1

1. (a) ∠z   (b) ∠EFG
   (c) ∠GFE
2. (a) ∠u   (b) ∠HIJ
   (c) ∠JIH
3. (a) ∠v   (b) ∠MNO
   (c) ∠ONM

4. (a) ∠w   (b) ∠KLM
   (c) ∠MLK
5. (a) ∠y   (b) ∠PQR
   (c) ∠RQP

Exercise 2

1. $p = 55°$ 2. $q = 40°$
3. $r = 120°$ 4. $s = 145°$

Exercise 3

1. 180°, 2   2. 90°,1
3. 270°, 3

Exercise 4

1. (a)   (b)

   (c)

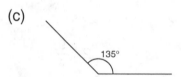

   (d)

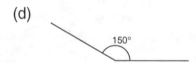

Chapter 6

Exercise 1

1. AB, BC   2. EF, FG
3. (a) PQ, PS   (b) PS, SR
4. MO, PN

Exercise 2

1. (Accept all possible answers.)

2. X   •A

        Y

Exercise 3

1.

2.
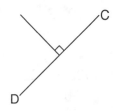

3.
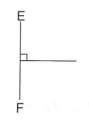

4.
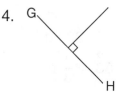

Exercise 4

1. AB, CD   2. PQ, RS
3. AB, DC
4. (a) EF, HG   (b) HE, GF
5. ST, RQ
6. BA, DC

Exercise 5

1. (Accept all possible answers.)

2.
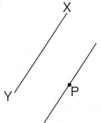

Exercise 6

1.
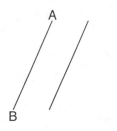

2.

3.
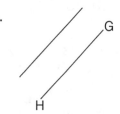

4.

Chapter 7

Exercise 1

1. (a) 5 cm   (b) 42 cm
2. (a) 30 cm   (b) 540 cm^2
3. (a) 12 cm   (b) 36 cm
   (c) 72 cm^2
4. (a) 14 cm   (b) 7 cm
   (c) 98 cm^2
5. (a) 15 cm   (b) 5 cm
   (c) 40 cm
6. 80 cm^2
7. (a) 96 m^2 (b) $960
8. 2400 m^2 (b) $8320

Exercise 2

1. (a) 24 cm   (b) 36 cm^2
2. (a) 10 cm   (b) 100 cm
3. (a) 8 cm   (b) 32 cm
4. (a) 15 cm   (b) 225 cm^2
5. (a) 20 m   (b) 400 m^2
6. (a) 100 cm^2 (b) 10 cm
   (c) 40 cm

Exercise 3

1. 48 cm

2. 54 cm

Exercise 4

1. 66 cm^2

2. 44 cm^2

Exercise 5

(a) 54 cm^2

(b) 42 cm

Exercise 6

(a) 108 cm^2

(b) 88 cm

Revision 2

1. (a) 1, 2, 4, 8, 16 and 32
   (b) 15, 30, 45, 60, 75
2. 140 litres
3.

4. PR and PQ
5. $250
6. (a) 60   (b) Soccer
   (c) 6   (d) Tennis
7. 100
8. 75
9. (a) 1650   (b) 2210
10. 43
11. 48 cm
12. 40 m^2
13. 100 cm
14. 80 cm
15. $3264
16. 18 cm
17. 216
18. 264

Mid-Year Examination

Section A

1. 3   2. 2
3. 2   4. 4
5. 4   6. 4

7. 4   8. 3
9. 2   10. 4
11. 1   12. 4
13. 3   14. 4
15. 2   16. 2
17. 3   18. 2
19. 3   20. 2

Section B

21. 14 cm   22. 12
23. 9   24. 3
25. $232
26.

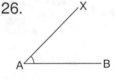

27. $\frac{1}{6}$ 28. 12 cm

29. $\frac{1}{3}, \frac{1}{2}, \frac{3}{5}, \frac{9}{10}$

30. 2565 ml   31. 28 kg

32. 62 509   33. $3\frac{1}{8}$ m

34. 70 m^2

35.

Type of book	Assessement books	Story books	Comic books	Other books
Number of books sold	80	100	20	120

Section C

36. 250
37. (a) $7200   (b) $400
38. (a) 30 m   (b) 240 m
39. $1.00
40.

41. 30

Enrichment Activities

1. 95°   2. 110°
3. 55°   4. 100°
5. 85°